Editor in Chief: Donna Battista
Assistant Editor: Kerri McQueen
Development Editor: Peter Lacey
Managing Editor: Jeff Holcomb
Senior Production Supervisor: Meredith Gertz
Senior Manufacturing Buyer: Carol Melville
Project Management, Composition, Illustrations, and Text Design: Gillian Hall, The Aardvark Group
Proofreader: Holly McLean-Aldis
Design Manager: Linda Knowles
Cover Designer: Susan Paradise
Cover Illustration: © Doug Rugh/Images.com/Corbis

D0126226

Prentice Hall
is an imprint of

www.pearsonhighered.com

ISBN-13: 978-0-13-609518-7
ISBN-10: 0-13-609518-6

2 3 4 5 6 7 8 9 10—CRS—13 12 11 10 09

MATH WORKBOOK

for
Personal
Financial Literacy